Verbiage for the Verbose

BLAH
Yadda
BLAH
BLAH
Yadda
Yadda
Yadda
BLAH
Yadda
BLAH
Yadda
BLAH

Verbiage for the Verbose

Unravel Over 250 Fun Word Challenges

Peter Gordon

Andrews McMeel Publishing
Kansas City

For information, write Andrews McMeel Publishing, an Andrews McMeel Universal company, 4520 Main Street, Kansas City, Missouri 64111.

www.andrewsmcmeel.com

98 99 00 01 02 BIN 10 9 8 7 6 5 4 3 2 1

Library of Congress Cataloging-in-Publications Data
Gordon, Peter
Verbiage for the verbose / Peter Gordon.
p. cm.
Contains over 250 well-known sayings, pop phrases, proverbs, etc. and a verbose rephrasing.
ISBN: 0-8362-5193-8 pb
1. American wit and humor. 2. English language—Terms and phrases—Humor. I. Title.
PN6231.W64G67 1998
818'.5402—DC21 97-34562
CIP

Design and composition by Mauna Eichner

To my more aged male sibling
Daniel, who at no time permits me to
cease to remember the method in
which I became engrossed by enigmas.

In other words...

To my big brother Dan,
who never lets me forget how I got
interested in puzzles.

Acknowledgments

Thanks to Merl, Andrew, Mike, Chrissy, Jesse, Eljay, Andy, Bill, Kaz, Sue, and Tom.

Verbiage for the Verbose

Common Phrases

All cumuli possess an argentic edging.

In Other Words

EVERY CLOUD HAS
A SILVER LINING.

Common Phrases

Do not enumerate one's domestic fowls prior to the end of their incubation period.

In Other Words

DON'T COUNT YOUR CHICKENS BEFORE THEY ARE HATCHED.

A naturally crystallized hard form of carbon is a young woman's closest companion.

In Other Words

A DIAMOND IS A GIRL'S BEST FRIEND.

A nincompoop and his currency are promptly sundered.

A FOOL AND HIS MONEY ARE SOON PARTED.

Possess mammals that use echolocation in one's tower for carillons.

In Other Words

HAVE BATS IN YOUR BELFRY.

Do not produce a bovine, sir.

DON'T HAVE A COW, MAN.

A pardine beast is unable to alter its markings.

In Other Words

A LEOPARD CAN'T
CHANGE HIS SPOTS.

A small amount of
erudition is a
hazardous matter.

A LITTLE KNOWLEDGE IS
A DANGEROUS THING.

Do not gaze into the muzzle of a thoroughbred that is a present.

DON'T LOOK A GIFT HORSE IN THE MOUTH.

I will submit a proposition that the man will be unable to say no to.

n Other Words

I'LL MAKE HIM AN OFFER HE CAN'T REFUSE.

A cupreous mintage
squirreled away is a
cupreous mintage netted.

In Other Words

A PENNY SAVED IS A
PENNY EARNED.

If the foot apparel is the correct size for one's foot, one should put it on.

IF THE SHOE FITS, WEAR IT.

A gyrating dornick
does not accumulate
bryophytic growth.

A ROLLING STONE
GATHERS NO MOSS.

A prickly-stemmed, pinnate-leaved, showy flower called something else would have the same pleasant fragrance.

In Other Words

A ROSE BY ANY OTHER NAME WOULD SMELL AS SWEET.

Do not nip at the manual extremity that nourishes you.

DON'T BITE THE HAND THAT FEEDS YOU.

An eyed cooking vessel will under no circumstances reach 212 degrees Fahrenheit.

A WATCHED POT NEVER BOILS.

A lupine beast in the raiments of an ovine beast.

A WOLF IN SHEEP'S CLOTHING.

Common Phrases

Watch out for Athenians carrying presents.

In Other Words

BEWARE OF GREEKS BEARING GIFTS.

Deeds communicate more forcibly than speech.

In Other Words

ACTIONS SPEAK LOUDER THAN WORDS.

Combat a blaze using
a blaze.

In Other Words

FIGHT FIRE WITH FIRE.

Everything that
coruscates is not auric.

In Other Words

ALL THAT GLITTERS
IS NOT GOLD.

Mendicants cannot be selectors.

In Other Words

BEGGARS CAN'T BE CHOOSERS.

Everything is permissible in affairs of the heart and combat.

In Other Words

ALL'S FAIR IN LOVE AND WAR.

Common Phrases

Repeatedly a female member of a wedding party, at no time a woman getting married.

In Other Words

ALWAYS A BRIDESMAID,
NEVER A BRIDE.

A certain pome every twenty-four-hour period holds the physician in abeyance.

AN APPLE A DAY KEEPS
THE DOCTOR AWAY.

An infantry walks
in formation on its
food-digesting organ.

AN ARMY MARCHES
ON ITS STOMACH.

It is impossible to
extract red bodily fluid
from a boulder.

In Other Words

YOU CAN'T GET BLOOD
FROM A STONE.

Whatever harbor in a tempest.

In Other Words

ANY PORT IN A STORM.

Make a doglike sound toward the incorrect woody plant.

In Other Words

BARK UP THE WRONG TREE.

A duad of craniums is superior to a single cranium.

TWO HEADS ARE BETTER THAN ONE.

Pulchritude extends merely to the epidermal layer.

In Other Words

BEAUTY IS ONLY SKIN DEEP.

The entire globe
is a rostrum.

ALL THE WORLD'S A STAGE.

It is preferable to be tardy than not to show up at all.

In Other Words

BETTER LATE THAN NEVER.

Being cautious is superior to being rueful.

BETTER SAFE THAN SORRY.

Nonattendance causes the cardiac organ to become more affectionate.

In Other Words

ABSENCE MAKES THE HEART GROW FONDER.

Flying beasts of a plume gather with one another.

BIRDS OF A FEATHER FLOCK TOGETHER.

Do not use one's teeth to separate an amount larger than one is able to masticate.

In Other Words

DON'T BITE OFF MORE THAN YOU CAN CHEW.

A satisfactory fellow is difficult to locate.

A GOOD MAN IS HARD TO FIND.

Plasma is more viscous than H_2O.

In Other Words

BLOOD IS THICKER THAN WATER.

Delivered through the birth canal with a utensil of element 47 in one's oral cavity.

In Other Words

BORN WITH A SILVER SPOON IN YOUR MOUTH.

Yadda Yadda BLAH BLAH

If you recline with hounds, you are going to rise with blood-sucking insects.

In Other Words

IF YOU LIE DOWN WITH DOGS, YOU WILL GET UP WITH FLEAS.

Common Phrases

Take the pig meat to one's residence.

In Other Words

BRING HOME THE BACON.

Construct a superior rodent-capturing device and everyone will make a trail to your portal.

BUILD A BETTER MOUSETRAP AND THE WORLD WILL BEAT A PATH TO YOUR DOOR.

Ignite the wax light with a wick at the two termini.

BURN THE CANDLE
AT BOTH ENDS.

At no time is it so delayed that one cannot become more educated.

In Other Words

IT'S NEVER TOO LATE TO LEARN.

Sweets are fine, however alcohol is faster.

In Other Words

CANDY IS DANDY, BUT
LIQUOR IS QUICKER.

Throw lustrous beads from mollusks in front of pigs.

In Other Words

CAST PEARLS BEFORE SWINE.

Permit the tabby beyond the confines of the sack.

LET THE CAT OUT OF THE BAG.

Swindlers don't ever thrive.

In Other Words

CHEATERS NEVER PROSPER.

Persevere with your organ with nostrils by the sharpening rock.

KEEP YOUR NOSE TO THE GRINDSTONE.

Frigid palms, generous blood-pumping organ.

In Other Words

COLD HANDS, WARM HEART.

Common Phrases

Emerge having the scent of New York's state flower.

In Other Words

COME OUT SMELLING LIKE A ROSE.

Admission of sins is
beneficent for the spirit.

In Other Words

CONFESSION IS GOOD
FOR THE SOUL.

Yours truly wept the entire distance to the money depository.

In Other Words

I CRIED ALL THE WAY TO THE BANK.

Inquisitiveness
caused the death of the
purring animal.

In Other Words

CURIOSITY KILLED THE CAT.

Slice away one's smelling organ to annoy one's countenance.

CUT OFF YOUR NOSE
TO SPITE YOUR FACE.

Deceased males do not relate stories.

In Other Words

DEAD MEN TELL NO TALES.

Do not substitute stallions in the center of a creek.

In Other Words

DON'T CHANGE HORSES IN MIDSTREAM.

A domestic fowl in each metal cooking container.

In Other Words

A CHICKEN IN EVERY POT.

Do not traverse a viaduct before arriving at it.

DON'T CROSS THE BRIDGE UNTIL YOU COME TO IT.

Do not pull the trigger prior to spotting their scleras.

In Other Words

DON'T FIRE UNTIL YOU SEE THE WHITES OF THEIR EYES.

An equine of another hue.

In Other Words

A HORSE OF A DIFFERENT COLOR.

Do not allow the wingless hemipterous insects to make an incision.

DON'T LET THE BEDBUGS BITE.

A pointed metal stitching rod in a mound of farm forage.

In Other Words

A NEEDLE IN A HAYSTACK.

Do not place every one of your reproductive bodies produced by birds in a single container.

In Other Words

DON'T PUT ALL YOUR EGGS IN ONE BASKET.

The flier that is ahead of time acquires the vermiform creature.

THE EARLY BIRD GETS THE WORM.

Do not place the dray
in front of the large,
solid-hoofed quadruped.

DON'T PUT THE CART
BEFORE THE HORSE.

The writing implement that uses ink is stronger than the blade.

n Other Words

THE PEN IS MIGHTIER THAN THE SWORD.

Do not dispose of the infant when disposing of the liquid in the tub.

In Other Words

DON'T THROW THE BABY OUT WITH THE BATHWATER.

Retiring at a reasonable hour and arising around daybreak causes a guy to be salubrious, rich, and sagacious.

In Other Words

EARLY TO BED AND EARLY TO RISE, MAKES A MAN HEALTHY, WEALTHY, AND WISE.

Ingest, imbibe, and be full of cheer, because the next day you and I shall bite the dust.

In Other Words

EAT, DRINK, AND BE MERRY, FOR TOMORROW WE DIE.

A concatenation is merely as secure as its most fragile coupling.

A CHAIN IS ONLY AS STRONG AS ITS WEAKEST LINK.

Knowledge gained from past observances and encounters is the unsurpassed educator.

In Other Words

EXPERIENCE IS THE BEST TEACHER.

Thorough knowledge of a thing engenders disdain.

In Other Words

FAMILIARITY BREEDS CONTEMPT.

The complete orb of
candle material.

In Other Words

THE WHOLE BALL OF WAX.

Give food to a respiratory illness, withhold food from a febrile state.

In Other Words

FEED A COLD, STARVE A FEVER.

Every byway heads toward the capital of Italy.

ALL ROADS LEAD TO ROME.

Battle using a gum protuberance and the hard part of a fingertip.

FIGHT TOOTH AND NAIL.

Discoverers custodians,
misplacers criers.

FINDERS KEEPERS,
LOSERS WEEPERS.

Use rod and reel or disengage the lure.

FISH OR CUT BAIT.

Slay a pair of feathered friends using a single rock.

In Other Words

KILL TWO BIRDS WITH
ONE STONE.

Ninnies hurriedly enter in places that cherubs have apprehension to step.

In Other Words

FOOLS RUSH IN WHERE
ANGELS FEAR TO TREAD.

Pleasant items arrive in little parcels.

In Other Words

GOOD THINGS COME IN SMALL PACKAGES.

Extraordinary intellects ideate similarly.

GREAT MINDS THINK ALIKE.

Piece of fur from
the barking beast that
nipped you.

In Other Words

HAIR OF THE DOG
THAT BIT YOU.

Rapidity produces profligacy.

HASTE MAKES WASTE.

Possess a drone in one's Easter hat.

HAVE A BEE IN YOUR BONNET.

The human condition is similar to a carton of candies made from cacao.

LIFE IS LIKE A BOX OF CHOCOLATES.

Possess the top playing card in the arm part of one's shirt.

HAVE AN ACE UP YOUR SLEEVE.

One soup-eating utensil's worth of sucrose aids in the ingestion of pharmaceuticals.

A SPOONFUL OF SUGAR HELPS THE MEDICINE GO DOWN.

Possess different beasts
with gills to sauté.

HAVE OTHER FISH TO FRY.

Common Phrases

Keep an excessive number of ferric tools in the flame.

In Other Words

HAVE TOO MANY IRONS IN THE FIRE.

Woe adores companionship.

MISERY LOVES COMPANY.

A fellow that pauses is beyond hope.

HE WHO HESITATES IS LOST.

No adult male is a piece of earth surrounded by water.

In Other Words

NO MAN IS AN ISLAND.

Obverse side of the coin and I am victorious, reverse side and you are defeated.

n Other Words

HEADS I WIN, TAILS YOU LOSE.

Analogous to a fowl with
its skull lopped off.

In Other Words

LIKE A CHICKEN WITH
ITS HEAD CUT OFF.

Common Phrases

A costless midday meal does not exist.

THERE'S NO SUCH THING AS A FREE LUNCH.

A domicile is the place that the ticker is located.

In Other Words

HOME IS WHERE THE HEART IS.

Veraciousness is the superior protocol.

HONESTY IS THE BEST POLICY.

I would prefer to be a striking tool instead of the object struck.

I'D RATHER BE A HAMMER THAN A NAIL.

A one-cent coin
for your ideas.

A PENNY FOR YOUR THOUGHTS.

I am as angry as the devil's home, and I will not stand for it even a little bit longer.

In Other Words

I'M MAD AS HELL, AND I'M NOT GOING TO TAKE IT ANYMORE.

If it is possible for an occurrence to go amiss, then that is what is going to come to pass.

IF ANYTHING CAN GO WRONG, IT WILL.

Fabricate straw during the time that the nearest star illuminates.

MAKE HAY WHILE
THE SUN SHINES.

If something resembles a web-footed fowl in appearance, stride, and sound, then that's what it is.

In Other Words

IF IT LOOKS LIKE A DUCK,
WALKS LIKE A DUCK, AND
QUACKS LIKE A DUCK,
IT'S A DUCK.

An illustration has the value of fifty score terms.

In Other Words

A PICTURE IS WORTH A THOUSAND WORDS.

The most incredible item since evenly cut baked dough.

THE GREATEST THING SINCE SLICED BREAD.

If one cannot withstand the extremely high temperature, keep away from the food preparation room.

In Other Words

IF YOU CAN'T TAKE THE HEAT,
STAY OUT OF THE KITCHEN.

Shortness is the essence of humor.

In Other Words

BREVITY IS THE SOUL OF WIT.

Mimicry is the most earnest kind of exaltation.

IMITATION IS THE SINCEREST FORM OF FLATTERY.

Arriving similar to a leonine beast, leaving similar to a young sheep.

IN LIKE A LION, OUT LIKE A LAMB.

Without achiness, there is no advancement.

In Other Words

NO PAIN, NO GAIN.

Ferric rods do not form a penitentiary.

IRON BARS DO NOT
A PRISON MAKE.

A couple is required to do a Latin-American ballroom dance.

In Other Words

IT TAKES TWO TO TANGO.

Negotiations ahead of enjoyment.

In Other Words

BUSINESS BEFORE PLEASURE.

The problem lies not in the high temperature, but rather in the accompanying moisture in the air.

In Other Words

IT'S NOT THE HEAT, IT'S THE HUMIDITY.

Elderly warriors do not keel over; they merely evanesce.

OLD SOLDIERS NEVER DIE;
THEY ONLY FADE AWAY.

Maintain a rigid top mouth rim.

In Other Words

KEEP A STIFF UPPER LIP.

Young humans ought to be perceived by sense of sight and not by sense of sound.

In Other Words

CHILDREN SHOULD BE SEEN AND NOT HEARD.

Maintain your sight organ
on the spheroid.

KEEP YOUR EYE ON THE BALL.

Murder the anserine beast that brings forth the gilded shelled items.

In Other Words

KILL THE GOOSE THAT LAYS THE GOLDEN EGGS.

Waft similar to a grown caterpillar, prick similar to an apian insect.

In Other Words

FLOAT LIKE A BUTTERFLY,
STING LIKE A BEE.

Place a rectangular dowel with equal-length sides in a circular opening.

PUT A SQUARE PEG IN A ROUND HOLE.

Empower the purchaser
to watch out.

LET THE BUYER BEWARE.

Does the feline have your tasting organ?

In Other Words

CAT GOT YOUR TONGUE?

Existence is merely a deep, round dish of red-colored, fruits with pits.

In Other Words

LIFE IS JUST A BOWL OF CHERRIES.

Retain a small
flake of wood on one's
arm-torso joint.

HAVE A CHIP ON
YOUR SHOULDER.

Bolts from the sky do not ever hit two times in identical locales.

In Other Words

LIGHTNING NEVER STRIKES TWICE IN THE SAME PLACE.

Similar to a corrida animal in a store of ceramics.

LIKE A BULL IN A CHINA SHOP.

Hades doesn't have anger comparable to a rejected mature female.

In Other Words

HELL HATH NO FURY LIKE
A WOMAN SCORNED.

Disjoin the bread grain from the grain husks.

In Other Words

SEPARATE THE WHEAT FROM THE CHAFF.

Resembling a duad of green vegetables in a seed vessel.

LIKE TWO PEAS IN A POD.

Grab the male cow
by the pointed growth
on the head.

TAKE THE BULL BY THE HORNS.

Subsist by the saber, meet death by the saber.

LIVE BY THE SWORD,
DIE BY THE SWORD.

Every subject is unsure except the end of life and governmental levies.

In Other Words

NOTHING IS CERTAIN BUT DEATH AND TAXES.

Slack kissing parts are the downfall of sailing vessels.

In Other Words

LOOSE LIPS SINK SHIPS.

Fortuitous at poker,
unfortuitous in amour.

LUCKY AT CARDS,
UNLUCKY IN LOVE.

Create a peak from a small pile of dirt for an underground mammal.

In Other Words

MAKE A MOUNTAIN OUT
OF A MOLEHILL.

When something is not in
an out-of-order state,
do not attempt to repair it.

In Other Words

IF IT AIN'T BROKE,
DON'T FIX IT.

Homo sapiens do not exist solely on food made with flour.

In Other Words

MAN DOES NOT LIVE
BY BREAD ALONE.

A tiny pace for a male person, a huge jump for the human race.

ONE SMALL STEP FOR MAN, ONE GIANT LEAP FOR MANKIND.

Female horses consume
cereal grasses and female
deer consume cereal
grasses and small
young sheep consume
a climbing vine.

In Other Words

MARES EAT OATS AND
DOES EAT OATS AND
LITTLE LAMBS EAT IVY.

A guy that brawls and flees, might survive to have a brawl at a later date.

HE WHO FIGHTS AND RUNS AWAY, MAY LIVE TO FIGHT ANOTHER DAY.

Currency does not issue forth on large plants with bark.

In Other Words

MONEY DOESN'T GROW ON TREES.

Imitating animal perceive,
imitating animal act.

MONKEY SEE, MONKEY DO.

The cosmos detests a space entirely devoid of matter.

In Other Words

NATURE ABHORS A VACUUM.

Do not be a loan taker or a loan giver.

In Other Words

NEITHER A BORROWER
NOR A LENDER BE.

Lack of sound is like a precious metal.

SILENCE IS GOLDEN.

A mint besom whisks immaculately.

A NEW BROOM SWEEPS CLEAN.

Likable chaps end up losing the race.

NICE GUYS FINISH LAST.

The man who gives cash to the wind instrument player gets to name the song.

In Other Words

HE WHO PAYS THE PIPER CALLS THE TUNE.

A lack of current events is positive current events.

In Other Words

NO NEWS IS GOOD NEWS.

Common Phrases

In the nation of the sightless, the cyclopean guy is royalty.

In Other Words

IN THE COUNTRY OF THE BLIND, THE ONE-EYED MAN IS KING.

There is no point in bawling about lacteal liquid that has sloshed over the edge.

In Other Words

NO USE CRYING OVER SPILT MILK.

Insufficient space to gyrate a kitty.

In Other Words

NOT ENOUGH ROOM
TO SWING A CAT.

Take a glance prior
to jumping.

In Other Words

LOOK BEFORE YOU LEAP.

Enduring customs cease difficultly.

OLD HABITS DIE HARD.

The important thing is
not if you finish first or last,
but the method by
which you participate in
the competition.

In Other Words

IT'S NOT WHETHER YOU
WIN OR LOSE, IT'S HOW YOU
PLAY THE GAME.

A single gent's beef is a different gent's toxin.

ONE MAN'S MEAT IS ANOTHER MAN'S POISON.

A multitude of sets of fingers and thumbs produce facile labor.

MANY HANDS MAKE LIGHT WORK.

The right set of circumstances bangs on just a single occasion.

OPPORTUNITY KNOCKS BUT ONCE.

Greater enjoyment than a cask of primates.

MORE FUN THAN
A BARREL OF MONKEYS.

Common Phrases

Not within the realm of visibility, not in the subconscious.

In Other Words

OUT OF SIGHT, OUT OF MIND.

Beings that reside
in residences made
of a transparent
substance ought not
toss large pebbles.

PEOPLE WHO LIVE IN
GLASS HOUSES SHOULDN'T
THROW STONES.

Removed from the skillet
and into the inferno.

OUT OF THE FRYING PAN
AND INTO THE FIRE.

Follow the customs of that which you sermonize.

In Other Words

PRACTICE WHAT YOU PREACH.

Allow slumbering pooches to be recumbent.

In Other Words

LET SLEEPING DOGS LIE.

Set one's cash in the place one's tongue resides.

PUT YOUR MONEY WHERE YOUR MOUTH IS.

Precipitate two types of common house pets.

RAIN CATS AND DOGS.

Withhold the switch and
overindulge the offspring.

In Other Words

SPARE THE ROD AND
SPOIL THE CHILD.

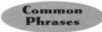

Regulations are created in order to be disobeyed.

In Other Words

RULES ARE MADE TO BE BROKEN.

Sock away for a time when there is a cloudburst.

In Other Words

SAVE FOR A RAINY DAY.

Visualize no wickedness,
pick up the sound of
no wickedness,
utter no wickedness.

In Other Words

SEE NO EVIL, HEAR NO EVIL, SPEAK NO EVIL.

The more massive that they are, the more forcibly they topple.

In Other Words

THE BIGGER THEY ARE, THE HARDER THEY FALL.

Sequester the grown males from the young males.

In Other Words

SEPARATE THE MEN
FROM THE BOYS.

More or less the same
as a swimming beast
not in fluid.

In Other Words

LIKE A FISH OUT OF WATER.

Display to me the legal tender.

In Other Words

SHOW ME THE MONEY.

Contradictory items have allure for each other.

In Other Words

OPPOSITES ATTRACT.

Common Phrases

Moderate and regular triumphs in the competition.

In Other Words

SLOW AND STEADY WINS THE RACE.

More intelligent than the normal ursine beast.

SMARTER THAN THE AVERAGE BEAR.

An ancient item,
a pristine item,
a temporarily
possessed item,
a cyan item.

SOMETHING OLD, SOMETHING
NEW, SOMETHING BORROWED,
SOMETHING BLUE.

Retaliation for wrongdoing is an entrée that is unsurpassed when presented unheated.

REVENGE IS A DISH BEST SERVED COLD.

Talk of Satan.

SPEAK OF THE DEVIL.

Did the domestic fowl exist before its offspring container, or vice versa?

In Other Words

WHICH CAME FIRST, THE CHICKEN OR THE EGG?

Branches and rocks
perhaps will cause
compound fractures in me.

In Other Words

STICKS AND STONES
MAY BREAK MY BONES.

Hit during the time that element 26 is scorching.

In Other Words

STRIKE WHILE THE IRON IS HOT.

Accept the acrid-tasting
with the sugary stuff.

TAKE THE BITTER
WITH THE SWEET.

Small ewers contain large handles.

LITTLE PITCHERS HAVE BIG EARS.

That which is acceptable for the male web-footed bird is acceptable for the female web-footed bird.

WHAT'S GOOD FOR THE GOOSE
IS GOOD FOR THE GANDER.

The red fruit does not drop off at a large distance from the orchard growth.

In Other Words

THE APPLE DOESN'T FALL FAR FROM THE TREE.

Common Phrases

Observing is accepting.

In Other Words

SEEING IS BELIEVING.

The male servant committed the crime.

In Other Words

THE BUTLER DID IT.

The product user is correct at all times.

THE CUSTOMER IS ALWAYS RIGHT.

Do not postpone until the next twenty-four-hour period that which can be accomplished in this twenty-four-hour period.

In Other Words

DON'T PUT OFF UNTIL
TOMORROW WHAT
YOU CAN DO TODAY.

Common Phrases

The lawn has, without fail, more chlorophyll on the opposite part of the property divider.

THE GRASS IS ALWAYS GREENER ON THE OTHER SIDE OF THE FENCE.

If desires were steeds, then panhandlers would be in the saddle.

IF WISHES WERE HORSES, THEN BEGGARS WOULD RIDE.

Do not accept even one five-cent piece made of lumber.

n Other Words

DON'T TAKE ANY WOODEN NICKELS.

The cauldron proclaiming the teapot ebony.

In Other Words

THE POT CALLING THE KETTLE BLACK.

The rapid,
chestnut-colored vulpine
beast leaps above
the slothful mongrel.

THE QUICK BROWN FOX JUMPS
OVER THE LAZY DOG.

One cannot deem the worthiness of a text by perusing its stiff outer layer.

YOU CAN'T JUDGE A BOOK BY ITS COVER.

It is impossible to manufacture a pocketbook of material from a worm's filament by using the auditory apparatus of an adult female swine.

YOU CAN'T MAKE A SILK PURSE OUT OF A SOW'S EAR.

The stalk of grain that
fractured the
dromedary's spine.

THE STRAW THAT BROKE
THE CAMEL'S BACK.

The path to a gent's four-chambered pumping organ is via his belly.

THE WAY TO A MAN'S HEART IS THROUGH HIS STOMACH.

More rapid than a streaking projectile from a gun.

In Other Words

FASTER THAN A SPEEDING BULLET.

There is integrity amidst pilferers.

In Other Words

THERE IS HONOR AMONG THIEVES.

Tread lightly and tote a large club.

In Other Words

WALK SOFTLY AND CARRY A BIG STICK.

There is in excess of a single method to remove the hide of a feline.

In Other Words

THERE'S MORE THAN ONE WAY TO SKIN A CAT.

Bang the spike on
the top part.

HIT THE NAIL ON THE HEAD.

Common Phrases

To make a mistake is mortal, to pardon is godlike.

In Other Words

TO ERR IS HUMAN,
TO FORGIVE DIVINE.

One can nab a greater quantity of flying insects with a viscid fluid made by bees than with acetic acid.

In Other Words

YOU CAN CATCH MORE
FLIES WITH HONEY
THAN WITH VINEGAR.

Reality is odder than fabrication.

TRUTH IS STRANGER THAN FICTION.

Comeliness lies within the perception of the observer.

In Other Words

BEAUTY IS IN THE EYE
OF THE BEHOLDER.

Common Phrases

A dupe is birthed each period of sixty seconds.

In Other Words

THERE'S A SUCKER
BORN EVERY MINUTE.

Room dividers possess hearing organs.

WALLS HAVE EARS.

That which moves toward the heavens at some point necessarily will reverse direction.

In Other Words

WHAT GOES UP MUST
COME DOWN.

Such is the manner that the baked treat falls apart.

THAT'S THE WAY THE COOKIE CRUMBLES.

It isn't possible to create a popular breakfast dish and not crack the main ingredients in the dish.

YOU CAN'T MAKE AN OMELET WITHOUT BREAKING EGGS.

A place that has the visible vapor from combustion also has combustion.

In Other Words

WHERE THERE'S SMOKE THERE'S FIRE.

Be prominent à la an aching opposable digit.

STICK OUT LIKE A SORE THUMB.

What is the point of purchasing a grown heifer if one has the ability to receive the liquid lactose it produces at no charge?

In Other Words

WHY BUY A COW WHEN YOU CAN
GET THE MILK FOR FREE?

You are the daylight of
my existence.

YOU ARE THE SUNSHINE
OF MY LIFE.

A superabundance of culinarians vitiates the bouillon.

TOO MANY COOKS SPOIL THE BROTH.

One is able to bring an equine mammal to potable liquid, but one does not have the ability to force it to imbibe.

In Other Words

YOU CAN LEAD A HORSE TO WATER, BUT YOU CAN'T MAKE IT DRINK.

Four hundred thirty-seven and a half grains of prophylaxis equals a little less than half a kilogram of antidote.

AN OUNCE OF PREVENTION IS WORTH A POUND OF CURE.

One cannot possess one's baked dessert and consume it as well.

YOU CAN'T HAVE YOUR CAKE AND EAT IT TOO.

The showers in
Madrid's country
descend predominantly
on the flatland.

In Other Words

THE RAIN IN SPAIN FALLS
MAINLY ON THE PLAIN.

Common Phrases

While the meowing animal is not present, the small rodents will frolic.

In Other Words

WHEN THE CAT'S AWAY, THE MICE WILL PLAY.

It is impossible to inculcate unfamiliar mannerisms to an elderly canine.

In Other Words

YOU CAN'T TEACH AN OLD DOG NEW TRICKS.

The creaking rotating item receives the lubricant.

In Other Words

THE SQUEAKY WHEEL GETS THE GREASE.

An avian beast in the
dactylic extremity
has the equivalent value
of a brace of them in
the shrubbery.

A BIRD IN THE HAND IS
WORTH TWO IN THE BUSH.

Television

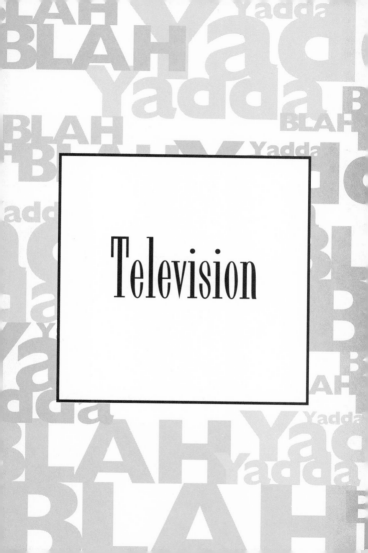

Five Dozen Short Units of Time

In Other Words

60 Minutes

Encounter the Fourth Estate

In Other Words

Meet the Press

Unrehearsed Photography Apparatus

Candid Camera

Diminutive Dwelling on the Grassland

In Other Words

Little House on the Prairie

Residence Refurbishment

In Other Words

Home Improvement

The Valuation Is Accurate

In Other Words

The Price Is Right

The Whitish-Red Cougar

Kindly Do Not Swallow the Yellow and White Flowers

In Other Words

Please Don't Eat the Daisies

The Gloaming Region

In Other Words

The Twilight Zone

Movies

The Carnivorous Feline Monarch

In Other Words

The Lion King

Factual Fabrications

In Other Words

True Lies

The Bird of Prey
from Valletta

The Maltese Falcon

Infuriated Taurine Beast

Raging Bull

Sovereign of the Drosophilas

In Other Words

Lord of the Flies

Movies

The Palm That Gently Shakes the Crib

In Other Words

The Hand That Rocks The Cradle

Prevaricator Prevaricator

In Other Words

Liar Liar

The Lack of Sound of the Young Ovine Beasts

The Silence of the Lambs

Boogies with Wild Dogs

In Other Words

Dances with Wolves

My Sinistral Leg Appendage

In Other Words

My Left Foot

The Hue of Cash

In Other Words

The Color of Money

Osculation of the Arachnid Female

In Other Words

Kiss of the Spider Woman

The King of the Jungle in the Cold Season

In Other Word

The Lion in Winter

The Wine Fruits of Anger

The Grapes of Wrath

Element 33 and
Vintage Netlike
Ornamental Fabric

Arsenic and Old Lace

Not Having Shoes or Socks on in the Recreation Area

Barefoot in the Park

A Heptad of Women to Be Married for a Heptad of Male Siblings

In Other Words

Seven Brides for Seven Brothers

An Unspecified Number Prefer It Toasty

Some Like It Hot

Nonacquaintances
on a Locomotive

In Other Words

Strangers on a Train

Movies

A Triad of Monetary Pieces in the Water Spray

n Other Words

Three Coins in the Fountain

Violinist on the Top of a House

In Other Words

Fiddler on the Roof

One Dozen Irate Fellows

12 Angry Men

Crooning in the Downpour

In Other Words

Singin' in the Rain

Tabby on a High Temperature Housetop Made of Element Sn

Cat on a Hot Tin Roof

A Little Less Than Half a Week of the Endangered Vulture

In Other Words

Three Days of the Condor

Movies

The Guy Carrying the Pistol Made of Element Au

In Other Words

The Man with the Golden Gun

A Heart of the Hot Season Late Part of the Day's Sleeping Thought

Yadda Yadda BLAH

The Wacky College Teacher

n Other Words

The Nutty Professor

Orbiting Body of the Primates

Planet of the Apes

The Espionage Agent That Entered from the Frigidness

The Spy Who Came in from the Cold

The Mail Carrier Without Fail Pushes the Doorbell Two Times

The Postman Always Rings Twice

The Moral, the Immoral, and the Hideous

The Good, the Bad, and the Ugly

A Third of a Dozen Nuptial Ceremonies and an Obsequy

Four Weddings and a Funeral

Songs

“The Pugilist”

“THE BOXER”

"I Have You Beneath My Epidermis"

In Other Words

"I've got you under my skin"

"Just the Virtuous Pass Away at an Early Age"

In Other Words

"ONLY THE GOOD DIE YOUNG"

“Undulating in the Zephyr”

“BLOWIN’ IN THE WIND”

“Xanthene Underwater Warship”

“YELLOW SUBMARINE”

“Soft-Cover Author”

In Other Words

“PAPERBACK WRITER”

Miscellaneous

Allow your digits to
perform the perambulating.

LET YOUR FINGERS DO THE WALKING. (*Yellow Pages*)

Every bit of information concerning the day's happenings that is worthy of publication.

ALL THE NEWS THAT'S FIT TO PRINT. (*New York Times*)

For the times that one has the desire to remit the absolute finest.

WHEN YOU CARE ENOUGH TO SEND THE VERY BEST.
(HALLMARK)

The Subfusc Hemisphere of the Lunar Body

The Dark Side of the Moon

The Thoroughfare Traversed Not as Frequently

In Other Words

The Road Less Traveled

The Baseball Receptor in the Seeded Bread

The Catcher in the Rye

Circle about the material at the neckline.

RING AROUND THE COLLAR.

(WISK)

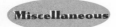

Apportion us seven days,
we will remove the
excessive poundage.

In Other Words

GIVE US A WEEK,
WE'LL TAKE OFF THE WEIGHT.
(ULTRA SLIM-FAST)

Place a striped cat in your gasoline holder.

PUT A TIGER IN YOUR TANK.
(EXXON)

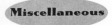

Be airborne in the
amicable stratospheres.

FLY THE FRIENDLY SKIES.
(UNITED)

About the Author

Peter Gordon is a scribe who resides in the Big Apple. He was a full-time redactor of enigmas for a period of two twelvemonths and a quinquennium at the bimonthly *Games*. His work as a cruciverbalist has been printed in numerous periodicals. His pastimes include kegling, deltiology, and sesquipedalianism. *Verbiage for the Verbose* is Gordon's debut bound publication.

In other words...

Peter Gordon is a writer who lives in New York City. He worked as a magazine puzzle editor for seven years at *Games*. His crossword puzzles have appeared in many newspapers and magazines. Some of his hobbies are bowling, postcard collecting, and using multisyllabic words. This is his first book.

About the Author

Peter Gordon is a scribe who resides in the Big Apple. He was a full-time redactor of enigmas for a period of two twelvemonths and a quinquennium at the bimonthly *Games*. His work as a cruciverbalist has been printed in numerous periodicals. His pastimes include kegling, deltiology, and sesquipedalianism. *Verbiage for the Verbose* is Gordon's debut bound publication.

In other words...

Peter Gordon is a writer who lives in New York City. He worked as a

magazine puzzle editor for seven years
at *Games*. His crossword puzzles
have appeared in many newspapers
and magazines. Some of his hobbies
are bowling, postcard collecting,
and using multisyllabic words.
This is his first book.